GRATITUDE
&
Girlfriends
JOURNAL

DR. KIMBERLY ELLISON & TRACY GRIMES

Gratitude & Girlfriends Journal
©2022 Sparkle Publishing All rights reserved.

ISBN: 978-1-954595-26-2

Sparkle Publishing Company
www.sparklepublishing.net

DEDICATION

This Gratitude and Girlfriends Journal is dedicated to every woman who has made it through life's most challenging seasons because of the girlfriends who've walked alongside her.

The Definition
GRATITUDE & GIRLFRIENDS

Gratitude
the quality of being thankful; readiness to show appreciation for and to return kindness.

Girlfriend
a bond shared between women that do life together.

GRATITUDE & GIRLFRIENDS

DR. KIMBERLY & *Tracy G.*

Why Gratitude & Girlfriends

Life has its way of providing solutions to situations we never knew we'd encounter, nor raise our hand and volunteer to go through. Somewhere along my journey, I heard someone say, "The only thing constant in life is change," and life has proven this statement to be true and since change is inevitable I've learned to embrace it with gratitude, grit, and grace. This hasn't always been my framework, however, at one point in my life I'd experienced so much change I had no choice but to thank God for allowing me to get through each situation without losing myself or my mind. I learned some of my best fighting techniques while life had me pinned up in what seemed like a full cobra clutch bulldog wrestling move. It was in those seasons I experienced His grace and developed the grit to not only go through it but get through it!

If I can be honest, expressing gratitude didn't change my situation, however, it did change how I went through every situation. As much as I felt alone, I often realized I wasn't. Not only did life situations and circumstances bring change, each season brought women into my life who were assigned to me in that season. Like most women, I have friends from childhood, grade-school, college, work friends, and life-long friends whom I love and still can't figure out how I got so blessed to have them in my life. However, I found that each season brought me exactly who I needed at the time I needed them. This is why Gratitude and Girlfriends is not just a journal or girls night out, but a movement to remind us of that we're not alone and we don't do life alone. We have girlfriends who are assigned to us in every season who are ready to pray, talk, eat, walk, laugh, sing, cry, or simply be there with us as the seasons of life shift us into the women we're created to become.

GRATITUDE & GIRLFRIENDS

DR. KIMBERLY & *Tracy G.*

How it Came About

I remember it like it was yesterday. My family had just moved across the country; literally we moved from the east to west coast during the Covid-19 pandemic. It was the first day of school for my kids, in a new state and new city, with no family or friends. My daughter's fourth grade orientation had just ended and I was waiting outside in the hallway for her class to be dismissed from school when I saw a group of moms whose kids were in the same fourth grade class as my daughter. Since we were new to the school, I was looking to connect with some of the parents so I kind of inserted myself into the conversation by asking their names and how long their kids had been at the school. Tracy, Krista, Tonya, and Aurora generously accepted my unsolicited insertion into their conversation. We shared our pleasantries and instantly connected as moms. I am not sure how the conversation came about, however, we began to talk about the demographics of race within the city and school. Where we live Blacks make-up about six percent of the 1.2 million people who live here so I looked at Tracy and asked her, "What are you?" After giving me the deepest sister girl neck roll she could give, she responded, "What do you mean, what am I? What are you?" We both laughed so hard we couldn't stop; it was like we'd known each other forever. Tracy looked at me and said, "I'm Black!" I said, "I know you are Black, but you have strong features resembling another ethnicity and I didn't want to make an assumption." She responded, "Girl, I am Black and Samoan." Again, we laughed so hard and I looked at her and said, "Girl, you know we're going to be friends because you are my kind of crazy!" We exchanged telephone numbers, Tracy invited me to breakfast the next morning and that was the beginning of our girlfriend season.

GRATITUDE & GIRLFRIENDS
DR. KIMBERLY & Tracy G.

How it Came About (continued)

As life would have it seven months later, I'm sitting in the doctor's office with my daughter who was unexpectedly and suddenly being transported via ambulance to the nearest Children's hospital. Keep in mind, we're in a new city with no family, my husband was on travel for work and my second grade son was still at school. I had no one to call and not a clue what to do. I looked at my phone and called Tracy. I am not sure of what I said or how clear I said it, but I told her I needed her help and I wasn't sure for how long. She said, "Say less, take care of McKinley and I will take care of Tripp. I will get him from school, wash his clothes, feed him, and make sure he has lunch for school tomorrow. He will be fine just focus on your daughter." I managed to hang up the phone, and I felt at peace. I knew God assigned Tracy and me to one another in this season for this moment. Since then we've experienced other life moments and have showed up for each other in our seasons. Gratitude and Girlfriends is about embracing every season with gratitude and the girlfriends assigned to your journey.

Gratitude & Girlfriends

HOW TO USE THIS JOURNAL

This Gratitude and Girlfriends Journal is divided into two sections:
(1) Gratitude and (2) Girlfriends.

The **Gratitude Section** of this journal is a form of self-care, designed to help you experience higher levels of appreciation, accountability, and action by expressing self-gratitude in the physical, mental, emotional, spiritual, financial, and professional areas of **your** life.

The **Girlfriends Section** of this journal is a form of gratitude, designed to help you express higher levels of appreciation, celebration, accountability, and action for the **girlfriends in your life** by sharing girlfriend tips, dos and don'ts, and ways to support your sisters that promote community and solidarity.

We are excited for you to begin your Gratitude and Girlfriends Journey!

TABLE OF CONTENTS

Self-Gratitude is Not Selfish! 11

Gratitude for My Family 29

Spiritual Gratitude 43

Gratitude Physical Health 59

Gratitude Emotional Well-Being 83

Financial Gratitude 101

Business & Career Gratitude 113

Gratitude Mental Health 123

Go-To Girlfriends 139

Gratitude for My Girls 149

Gratitude On a Budget 161

The Dos & Don'ts 175

Check On Your Strong Friends 183

Meet the Authors 197

THE GIFT OF *Gratitude*

DR. KIMBERLY ELLISON

Gratitude is a gift that should always be present in our lives. Not only is it important for us to express our gratitude to others, but also to ourselves. Girlfriend, you are a gift and your existence on this earth is something to be grateful for. Whether you know it or not, no matter what your journey has been, you are a warrior, a survivor, and a rare jewel who has survived 100 percent of your worst days and you deserve to celebrate your journey. Like most women, we do a great job of serving, catering, and filling the needs of everyone else, yet we leave little space to take care of ourselves. You've learned to have big energy while operating on fumes, you've managed to make every practice, recital, drop-off, birthday party, family, work, or church event while giving little thought to the energy and intentionality it takes for you to pour yourself out tirelessly. Sis, you are gift; your time and energy doesn't come without sacrifice, yet you often extend your gratitude to only those who have demonstrated acts of kindness to you and now it's time to appreciate and celebrate you. It's important that you become your own cheerleader, hype woman, and biggest fan. Giving yourself the gift of gratitude will help you to reflect, reconnect, and rejuvenate from the inside, out.

The gratitude section of this journal is a form of self-care, designed to help you experience higher levels of appreciation, accountability, and action by expressing self-gratitude in the physical, mental, emotional, spiritual, financial, and professional areas of your life. Girlfriend, this section is where you say, "I'd like to thank, me." Thank yourself for showing up and not giving up when you had valid reasons to do so. Thank yourself for the sacrifices you've made that grace makes look easy. Sister, as you turn each page, I encourage you to accept and embrace the gift of gratitude you are about to unwrap for yourself.

Girlfriend, it's time to give yourself the credit you deserve and pat yourself on the back! **Self-gratitude** is a practice that brings **awareness and appreciation** for who you are and what you give to the world. Practicing self-gratitude allows you to see your **growth** in every area of your life. It is both **reflective and reassuring** along your journey.

SELF-*Gratitude* IS NOT *Selfish!*

"

"WHEN IT COMES TO LIFE THE *critical* THING IS WHETHER YOU TAKE THINGS FOR *granted* OR TAKE THEM WITH *gratitude.*"

-G.K. Chesterton

TYPES OF
Self-Care
TO SHOW GRATITUDE TO YOURSELF!

01

SELF-CARE

Self-care is taking care of your self in every area of your life. It includes taking the time to connect with yourself to determine your needs and next steps. Self-care can bring clarity, renewed strength, revive your energy, and help ensure you remain healthy in your body, mind, and spirit.

02

PHYSICAL SELF-CARE

Learning to appreciate your body and its abilities and capabilities. It is important to take care of your body because there's a strong connection between your body and your mind.

03

EMOTIONAL SELF-CARE

Emotional self-care is allowing yourself to feel your emotions for what they are while generating an awareness for what you need.

04

MENTAL HEALTH SELF-CARE

This type of self-care focuses on your thought life. It should aim to stimulate your mind, protect your peace, and boost intellectual engagement.

05

SPIRITUAL SELF-CARE

This type of self-care is necessary for your journey. It should be both personal and a priority. It is about belief, connection, finding strength, and inner peace.

06

SOCIAL SELF-CARE

Spending time with others, whether that's friends or family, is important to your overall well-being, happiness and creates community.

07

FINANCIAL SELF-CARE

This type of self-care is about embracing your financial journey while learning to manage and maintain your financial goals and obligations. As well as thinking about your financial future.

SELF-*Gratitude* IS NOT *Selfish!*

All About Me!

My name is _____

I am _____ years old.

I am celebrating _____

I am excited about _____

_____

_____

Place Selfie Here

During my self-care time, I like to:

Books I want to read are:

I am happy when:

SELF-*Gratitude* IS NOT *Selfish!*
I am showing myself some love!

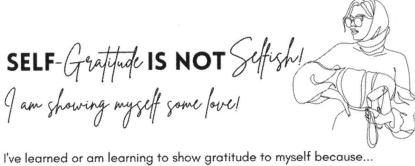

I've learned or am learning to show gratitude to myself because...

_____

_____

_____

_____

_____

Showing myself gratitude use to feel or feels uncomfortable to me because...

_____

_____

_____

_____

_____

I want to celebrate myself more by...

_____

_____

_____

_____

I will show myself gratitude today by...

_____

_____

_____

_____

SELF-*Gratitude* IS NOT *Selfish!*

I am showing myself some love!

I appreciate my abilty to...

_____
_____
_____
_____
_____

I am a powerhouse when it comes to...

_____
_____
_____
_____
_____

One thing I'm going to do is...

_____
_____
_____
_____
_____

I am no longer going to allow...

_____
_____
_____
_____
_____

SELF-*Gratitude* IS NOT *Selfish!*
I am showing myself some love!

I appreciate my abilty to...

_____

_____

_____

_____

_____

I am a powerhouse when it comes to...

_____

_____

_____

_____

_____

One thing I'm going to do is...

_____

_____

_____

_____

_____

I am no longer going to allow...

_____

_____

_____

_____

_____

MY *Self-Gratitude* BUCKET LIST

Below make a list of ways you want to show yourself some gratitude.

☐   Take an International Me-cation this year.

☐   _____

☐   _____

☐   _____

☐   _____

☐   _____

☐   _____

☐   _____

☐   _____

☐   _____

MY *Self-Gratitude* BUCKET LIST

Below make a list of ways you want to show yourself some gratitude.

☐   Take an International Me-cation this year.
_____

☐   _____
_____

☐   _____
_____

☐   _____
_____

☐   _____
_____

☐   _____
_____

☐   _____
_____

☐   _____
_____

☐   _____
_____

☐   _____

MY *Self-Gratitude* BUCKET LIST

Below make a list of ways you want to show yourself some gratitude.

☐ Take an International Me-cation this year.

☐

☐

☐

☐

☐

☐

☐

☐

☐

SELF-*Gratitude* IS NOT *Selfish!*
I AM GRATEFUL FOR...

Each day, reflect on people, places, or things you are grateful for in your life.
Below write down all the things you are grateful for today.

PEOPLE

1. _____

2. _____

3. _____

4. _____

5. _____

PLACES

1. _____

2. _____

3. _____

4. _____

5. _____

THINGS

1. _____

2. _____

3. _____

4. _____

5. _____

SELF-*Gratitude* IS NOT *Selfish!*
I AM GRATEFUL FOR...

Each day, reflect on people, places, or things you are grateful for in your life.
Below write down all the things you are grateful for today.

PEOPLE

1. _____
2. _____
3. _____
4. _____
5. _____

PLACES

1. _____
2. _____
3. _____
4. _____
5. _____

THINGS

1. _____
2. _____
3. _____
4. _____
5. _____

SELF-*Gratitude* IS NOT *Selfish!*
I AM GRATEFUL FOR...

Each day, reflect on people, places, or things you are grateful for in your life. Below write down all the things you are grateful for today.

PEOPLE

1. _____

2. _____

3. _____

4. _____

5. _____

PLACES

1. _____

2. _____

3. _____

4. _____

5. _____

THINGS

1. _____

2. _____

3. _____

4. _____

5. _____

GRATITUDE
&
Girlfriends
JOURNAL

GRATITUDE
&
Girlfriends
JOURNAL

GRATITUDE
&
Girlfriends
JOURNAL

Gratitude makes sense of our past, brings peace for today, and creates a vision for tomorrow.

- Melody Beattie

Gratitude

FOR MY FAMILY

"

THERE'S NO *fairy* TALE FAMILY, BUT THERE ARE PLENTY OF *magical* MOMENTS.

-Unknown

"

FOR MY FAMILY

Girlfriend, family is everything and let's be clear, there are no perfect families! Every family has its good, bad, and ugly moments, however it's more about going through each moment with those you love and those who love you. Whether you've experienced challenges or triumphs with family members, you've either learned a lesson or taught one. Write a statement of gratitude for each family member below.

Grandpa

_____

_____

_____

_____

Grandma

_____

_____

_____

_____

Dad

_____

_____

_____

_____

Mom

_____

_____

_____

_____

Gratitude

FOR MY FAMILY

Girlfriend, family is everything and let's be clear, there are no perfect families! Every family has its good, bad, and ugly moments, however it's more about going through each moment with those you love and those who love you. Whether you've experienced challenges or triumphs with family members, you've either learned a lesson or taught one. Write a statement of gratitude for each family member below.

Sister

_____

_____

_____

_____

Brother

_____

_____

_____

_____

Aunt

_____

_____

_____

_____

Uncle

Gratitude
FOR MY FAMILY
Lessons of gratitude from my family!

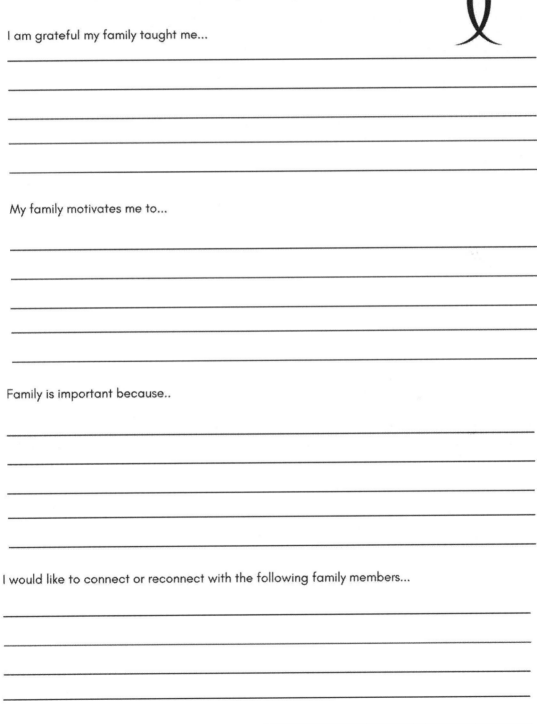

I am grateful my family taught me...

_____
_____
_____
_____
_____

My family motivates me to...

_____
_____
_____
_____
_____

Family is important because..

_____
_____
_____
_____
_____

I would like to connect or reconnect with the following family members...

_____
_____
_____
_____
_____

Gratitude
FOR MY FAMILY

Lessons of gratitude from my family!

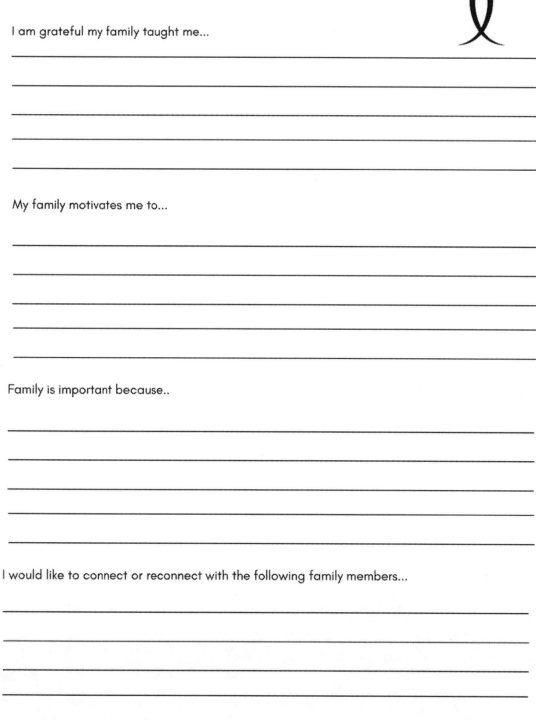

I am grateful my family taught me...

_____

_____

_____

_____

_____

My family motivates me to...

_____

_____

_____

_____

_____

Family is important because..

_____

_____

_____

_____

_____

I would like to connect or reconnect with the following family members...

_____

_____

_____

_____

_____

Gratitude
FOR MY FAMILY

Lessons of gratitude from my family!

I am grateful my family taught me...

_____

_____

_____

_____

_____

My family motivates me to...

_____

_____

_____

_____

_____

Family is important because..

_____

_____

_____

_____

I would like to connect or reconnect with the following family members...

_____

_____

_____

_____

_____

Gratitude
FOR MY FAMILY

Lessons of gratitude from my family!

I am grateful my family taught me...

_____

_____

_____

_____

_____

My family motivates me to...

_____

_____

_____

_____

_____

Family is important because..

_____

_____

_____

_____

_____

I would like to connect or reconnect with the following family members...

_____

_____

_____

_____

_____

Gratitude
FOR MY FAMILY

Lessons of gratitude from my family!

I am grateful my family taught me...

_____

_____

_____

_____

_____

My family motivates me to...

_____

_____

_____

_____

_____

Family is important because..

_____

_____

_____

_____

_____

I would like to connect or reconnect with the following family members...

_____

_____

_____

_____

_____

GRATITUDE
&
Girlfriends
JOURNAL

GRATITUDE
&
Girlfriends
JOURNAL

GRATITUDE
&
Girlfriends
JOURNAL

Gratitude is the act of feeling and communicating **appreciation** for the people, circumstances and material possessions in our lives. It allows us to **cherish** our **present** in ways that make us **feel in abundance** rather than deprived.

– Luis Romero

SPIRITUAL *Gratitude*

"

"LET *gratitude* BE THE PILLOW UPON WHICH YOU *kneel* TO SAY YOUR NIGHTLY PRAYER AND LET *faith* BE THE BRIDGE YOU BUILD TO OVERCOME EVIL AND WELCOME *good*."

–Maya Angelou

SPIRITUAL *Gratitude*

Spiritual gratitude is finding inner peace and truth through faith. We express spiritual gratitude when we pray, worship, praise, meditate, serve others, and spend intimate time in God's word.

Below, describe how you express spiritual gratitude through the following:

PRAYER

_____

_____

_____

_____

_____

FAITH

_____

_____

_____

_____

_____

MEDITATION

_____

_____

_____

_____

_____

SPIRITUAL *Gratitude*

Spiritual gratitude is finding inner peace and truth through faith. We express spiritual gratitude when we pray, worship, praise, meditate, serve others, and spend intimate time in God's word.

Below, describe how you express spiritual gratitude through the following:

PRAISE

_____
_____
_____
_____
_____

WORSHIP

_____
_____
_____
_____
_____

SERVING OTHERS

_____
_____
_____
_____
_____

SPIRITUAL *Gratitude* *Bible* STUDY PLANNER

Study Text: _____   Date: _____

KEY STUDY NOTES

_____

_____

_____

_____

_____

_____

_____

_____

IMPORTANT TOPICS   I AM GRATEFUL TO KNOW...

SPIRITUAL *Gratitude*
Bible STUDY PLANNER

Study Text: _____   Date: _____

KEY STUDY NOTES

_____

_____

_____

_____

_____

_____

_____

IMPORTANT TOPICS   I AM GRATEFUL TO KNOW...

SPIRITUAL *Gratitude*
Bible STUDY PLANNER

Study Text: ....   Date: ....

KEY STUDY NOTES

_____

_____

_____

_____

_____

_____

_____

IMPORTANT TOPICS   I AM GRATEFUL TO KNOW...

SPIRITUAL *Gratitude* *Bible* STUDY PLANNER

Study Text: _____ Date: _____

KEY STUDY NOTES

_____

_____

_____

_____

_____

_____

_____

IMPORTANT TOPICS   I AM GRATEFUL TO KNOW...

SPIRITUAL *Gratitude* *Bible* STUDY PLANNER

Study Text: .... Date: ....

KEY STUDY NOTES

....

....

....

....

....

....

....

....

....

....

IMPORTANT TOPICS   I AM GRATEFUL TO KNOW...

SPIRITUAL *Gratitude* *Bible* STUDY PLANNER

Study Text: _____ Date: _____

KEY STUDY NOTES

_____

_____

_____

_____

_____

_____

_____

IMPORTANT TOPICS   I AM GRATEFUL TO KNOW...

SPIRITUAL *Gratitude* *Bible* STUDY PLANNER

Study Text: _____   Date: _____

KEY STUDY NOTES

_____

_____

_____

_____

_____

_____

_____

IMPORTANT TOPICS   I AM GRATEFUL TO KNOW...

GRATITUDE
&
Girlfriends
JOURNAL

GRATITUDE
&
Girlfriends
JOURNAL

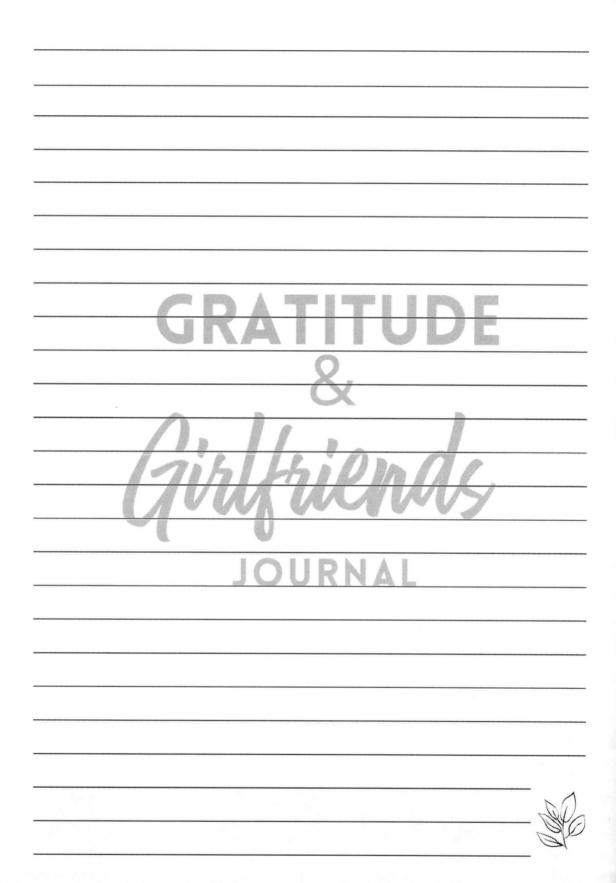

*A wise woman ought to realize that **health** is her most valuable possession." – Hippocrates (remixed)*

Gratitude

PHYSICAL HEALTH

"

"TAKE CARE OF YOUR *Body.* **IT'S THE ONLY PLACE YOU HAVE TO** *Live.* **"**

-John Rohn

Gratitude
MY PHYSICAL HEALTH

I am Body Goals!

Girl, stop it now! No more body shaming yourself or standing in the mirror wishing and wanting to have the perfect Instagram body. Sis, that's a filter! It's time to show your body some appreciation for everything it has been through and helped you get through. Your body is goals! It's bad, in a good way! Your body has been there with you through everything and believe or not, there are people who are willing to swap bodies with you at a moments notice. Girlfriend, embrace your shape and your size! Your body deserves to be loved and appreciated at every stage of your journey. You've changed, and just as the seasons of life bring change, our bodies change. If it is weight you want or need to lose, then lose it not because you dislike your body, but because you love it! If it's exercise, proper nutrition, sleeping well, staying hydrated, or sexual health, you will need to treat your body with the appreciation it deserves. You need your body to function at its best. Sis, show yourself some gratitude and take care of your physical health!

♥ Dr. Kimberly Ellison

DAILY
Affirmations

My body deserves love.

I am confident and comfortable in my own skin.

I am thankful for my ability to think for myself.

I am gentle with my body.

I am the best version of myself.

I'm grateful for my portion of health and strength.

Belly, thank you for helping me to digest.

Stretch marks, thank you for reminding me of how my body can endure change.

I make rest a priority in my life.

My body is beautiful just the way it is.

I will not compare myself to others.

I am beautiful, confident and loved.

I am aging gracefully.

I am in-tune with my femininity.

I am sexy at any size.

I give myself permission to heal.

I forgive myself for not taking the best care of my body.

I am grateful to feel.

My life is bigger than my size.

My body is a gift.

I trust the wisdom of my body.

I choose to love my body and treat it well.

Gratitude
MY PHYSICAL HEALTH

Appreciating My Body!

Today, I am feeling...

_____
_____
_____
_____
_____

I am grateful for my body because...

_____
_____
_____
_____

I need to remind myself...

_____
_____
_____
_____

I am taking better care of my physical health by...

_____
_____
_____
_____

Gratitude
MY PHYSICAL HEALTH

Appreciating My Body!

Today, I am feeling...

_____

_____

_____

_____

_____

I am grateful for my body because...

_____

_____

_____

_____

I need to remind myself...

_____

_____

_____

_____

I am taking better care of my physical health by...

_____

_____

_____

_____

_____

Gratitude
MY PHYSICAL HEALTH

Appreciating My Body!

Today, I am feeling...

_____
_____
_____
_____
_____

I am grateful for my body because...

_____
_____
_____
_____
_____

I need to remind myself...

_____
_____
_____
_____
_____

I am taking better care of my physical health by...

_____
_____
_____
_____
_____

Gratitude
MY PHYSICAL HEALTH

Appreciating My Body!

Today, I am feeling...

_____
_____
_____
_____
_____

I am grateful for my body because...

_____
_____
_____
_____
_____

I need to remind myself...

_____
_____
_____
_____
_____

I am taking better care of my physical health by...

_____
_____
_____
_____
_____

Gratitude
MY PHYSICAL HEALTH

Appreciating My Body!

Today, I am feeling...

_____
_____
_____
_____
_____

I am grateful for my body because...

_____
_____
_____
_____
_____

I need to remind myself...

_____
_____
_____
_____
_____

I am taking better care of my physical health by...

_____
_____
_____
_____
_____

Gratitude
MY PHYSICAL HEALTH

Appreciating My Body!

Today, I am feeling...

_____
_____
_____
_____
_____

I am grateful for my body because...

_____
_____
_____
_____
_____

I need to remind myself...

_____
_____
_____
_____
_____

I am taking better care of my physical health by...

_____
_____
_____
_____
_____

Gratitude
MY PHYSICAL HEALTH

Appreciating My Body!

Today, I am feeling...

_____
_____
_____
_____
_____

I am grateful for my body because...

_____
_____
_____
_____
_____

I need to remind myself...

_____
_____
_____
_____
_____

I am taking better care of my physical health by...

_____
_____
_____
_____
_____

Gratitude
MY PHYSICAL HEALTH

With L♥ve,

To experience a higher level of gratitude, write a love letter to your body. Focus on telling your body a new story, one that comes from a place of ***apology, appreciation, compassion and growth.***

To my beautiful body,

 **All of my love,**

Your Signature

PHYSICAL HEALTH *Tracker*

MY PHYSICAL ACTIVITY FOR TODAY

- ▶ _____
- ▶ _____
- ▶ _____
- ▶ _____

LIST OF EXERCISE

- ▶ _____
- ▶ _____
- ▶ _____
- ▶ _____

HEALTHY FOOD CHOICES OR BETTER CHOICES

- ▶ _____
- ▶ _____
- ▶ _____
- ▶ _____

NOTES   ▶ _____

_____

_____

MY GOALS FOR TODAY

DRINK MY WATER

71

PHYSICAL HEALTH *Tracker*

MY PHYSICAL ACTIVITY FOR TODAY

▶ _____

▶ _____

▶ _____

▶ _____

LIST OF EXERCISE

▶ _____

▶ _____

▶ _____

▶ _____

HEALTHY FOOD CHOICES OR BETTER CHOICES

▶ _____

▶ _____

▶ _____

▶ _____

NOTES   ▶ _____

_____

_____

MY GOALS FOR TODAY

DRINK MY WATER

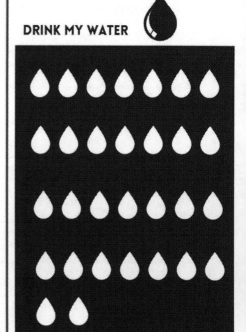

PHYSICAL HEALTH *Tracker*

MY PHYSICAL ACTIVITY FOR TODAY

▶ _____

▶ _____

▶ _____

▶ _____

LIST OF EXERCISE

▶ _____

▶ _____

▶ _____

▶ _____

HEALTHY FOOD CHOICES OR BETTER CHOICES

▶ _____

▶ _____

▶ _____

▶ _____

NOTES   ▶ _____

_____

_____

MY GOALS FOR TODAY

DRINK MY WATER

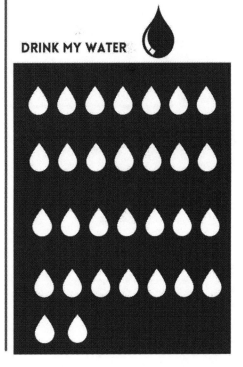

PHYSICAL HEALTH *Tracker*

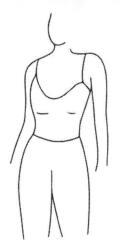

MY PHYSICAL ACTIVITY FOR TODAY

▶ _____

▶ _____

▶ _____

▶ _____

LIST OF EXERCISE

▶ _____

▶ _____

▶ _____

▶ _____

HEALTHY FOOD CHOICES OR BETTER CHOICES

▶ _____

▶ _____

▶ _____

▶ _____

NOTES   ▶ _____

_____

_____

MY GOALS FOR TODAY

DRINK MY WATER

PHYSICAL HEALTH *Tracker*

MY PHYSICAL ACTIVITY FOR TODAY

▶ _____

▶ _____

▶ _____

▶ _____

LIST OF EXERCISE

▶ _____

▶ _____

▶ _____

▶ _____

HEALTHY FOOD CHOICES OR BETTER CHOICES

▶ _____

▶ _____

▶ _____

▶ _____

NOTES   ▶ _____

_____

_____

MY GOALS FOR TODAY

DRINK MY WATER

PHYSICAL
HEALTH *Tracker*

MY PHYSICAL ACTIVITY FOR TODAY

▶ _____

▶ _____

▶ _____

▶ _____

LIST OF EXERCISE

▶ _____

▶ _____

▶ _____

▶ _____

HEALTHY FOOD CHOICES OR BETTER CHOICES

▶ _____

▶ _____

▶ _____

▶ _____

NOTES   ▶ _____

_____

_____

MY GOALS FOR TODAY

DRINK MY WATER

PHYSICAL HEALTH *Tracker*

MY PHYSICAL ACTIVITY FOR TODAY

▶ _____

▶ _____

▶ _____

▶ _____

LIST OF EXERCISE

▶ _____

▶ _____

▶ _____

▶ _____

HEALTHY FOOD CHOICES OR BETTER CHOICES

▶ _____

▶ _____

▶ _____

▶ _____

NOTES   ▶ _____

_____

_____

MY GOALS FOR TODAY

DRINK MY WATER

GRATITUDE
&
Girlfriends
JOURNAL

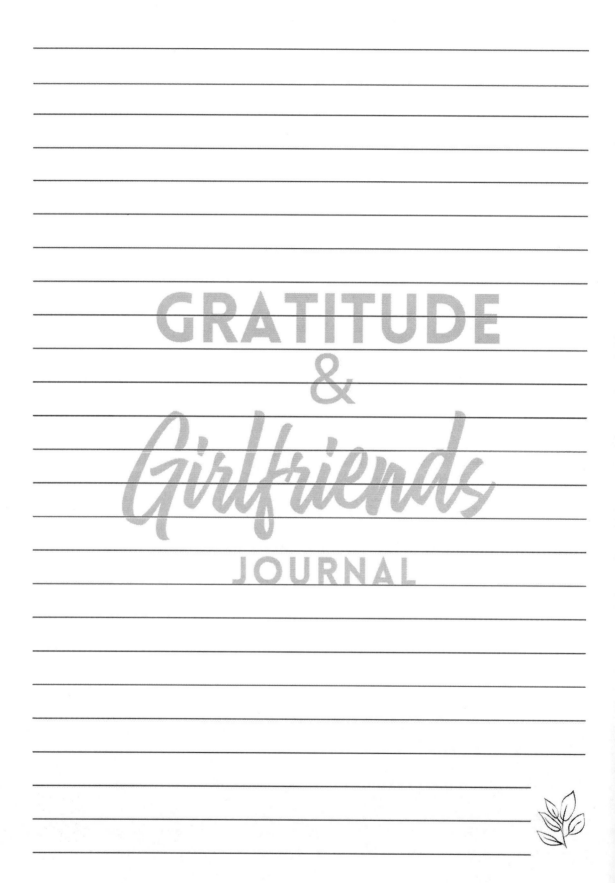

GRATITUDE
&
Girlfriends
JOURNAL

GRATITUDE
&
Girlfriends
JOURNAL

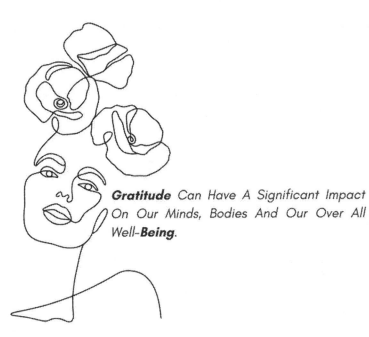

Gratitude *Can Have A Significant Impact On Our Minds, Bodies And Our Over All Well-**Being**.*

EMOTIONAL WELL-BEING

Gratitude

66

EMOTIONAL HEALTH IS ABOUT HOW WE *Think* AND FEEL. IT IS ABOUT OUR SENSE OF WELL-BEING, OUR ABILITY TO COPE WITH LIFE EVENTS AND HOW WE ACKNOWLEDGE OUR OWN *Emotions* AS WELL AS THOSE OF OTHERS.

-Samaritans Charity

GRATITUDE FOR EMOTIONAL *Growth!*

Girlfriend, listen up, your emotional well-being is critical to getting over and through some of life's unsolicited and unforeseen challenges. Let's face it, sometimes your emotions get the best of you and you react instead of respond, however, the more aware you are of your emotions the more you are able to manage your emotions during difficult times. Sis, you've grown, you're no longer the same person, you no longer react to situations the same, but you haven't taken the time to reflect and celebrate your emotional growth. Friend, it's time to take personal inventory of your emotions and express your gratitude for how you've learned to manage your emotions and not let your emotions manage you!

Old Me: Describe how you use to react when certain emotions were triggered.

New Me: Describe how you respond now when those same emotions are triggered.

Girl, I am in my feelings today!

MY DAILY EMOTIONS LOG

Choose two to three words from the list to describe how you feel today. Write them in the blank space below. Can't find your emotions there? Feel free to use other words.

Today's Date:

I think these feelings are:

○ both positive   ○ positive and negative

○ negative and positive   ○ both negative

I feel this way because _____

_____

_____

_____

_____

_____

_____

_____

_____

What do I need to manage my emotions today?

_____

_____

_____

_____

_____

EMOTIONS LIST
angry
annoyed
anxious
ashamed
awkward
brave
calm
cheerful
chill
confused
discouraged
disgusted
distracted
embarrassed
excited
friendly
guilty
happy
hopeful
jealous
lonely
loved
nervous
offended
scared
thoughtful
tired
uncomfortable
unsure
worried

Managing My Emotions

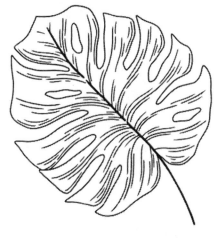

How did I react or respond today?

_____

_____

_____

_____

_____

What triggered my reaction or prompted my response?

_____

_____

_____

_____

_____

I am proud of myself because...

_____

_____

_____

_____

_____

I am grateful for...

_____

_____

_____

_____

_____

Girl, I am in my feelings today!

MY DAILY EMOTIONS LOG

Choose two to three words from the list to describe how you feel today. Write them in the blank space below. Can't find your emotions there? Feel free to use other words.

Today's Date:

I think these feelings are:

○ both positive   ○ positive and negative

○ negative and positive   ○ both negative

I feel this way because _____

_____

_____

_____

_____

_____

_____

_____

_____

What do I need to manage my emotions today?

_____

_____

_____

_____

_____

_____

_____

EMOTIONS LIST
angry
annoyed
anxious
ashamed
awkward
brave
calm
cheerful
chill
confused
discouraged
disgusted
distracted
embarrassed
excited
friendly
guilty
happy
hopeful
jealous
lonely
loved
nervous
offended
scared
thoughtful
tired
uncomfortable
unsure
worried

Managing My Emotions

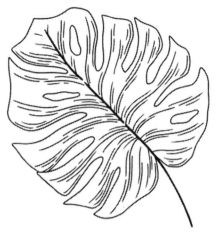

How did I react or respond today?

_____
_____
_____
_____
_____

What triggered my reaction or prompted my response?

_____
_____
_____
_____
_____

I am proud of myself because...

_____
_____
_____
_____

I am grateful for...

_____
_____
_____
_____

Girl, I am in my feelings today!

MY DAILY EMOTIONS LOG

Choose two to three words from the list to describe how you feel today. Write them in the blank space below. Can't find your emotions there? Feel free to use other words.

Today's Date:

I think these feelings are:

○ both positive   ○ positive and negative
○ negative and positive ○ both negative

I feel this way because _____

_____

_____

_____

_____

_____

_____

_____

_____

What do I need to manage my emotions today?

_____

_____

_____

_____

_____

_____

EMOTIONS LIST
angry
annoyed
anxious
ashamed
awkward
brave
calm
cheerful
chill
confused
discouraged
disgusted
distracted
embarrassed
excited
friendly
guilty
happy
hopeful
jealous
lonely
loved
nervous
offended
scared
thoughtful
tired
uncomfortable
unsure
worried

Managing My Emotions

How did I react or respond today?

_____

_____

_____

_____

_____

What triggered my reaction or prompted my response?

_____

_____

_____

_____

_____

I am proud of myself because...

_____

_____

_____

_____

_____

I am grateful for...

_____

_____

_____

_____

_____

Girl, I am in my feelings today!

MY DAILY EMOTIONS LOG

Choose two to three words from the list to describe how you feel today. Write them in the blank space below. Can't find your emotions there? Feel free to use other words.

Today's Date:

I think these feelings are:

○ both positive   ○ positive and negative
○ negative and positive ○ both negative

I feel this way because _____

_____

_____

_____

_____

_____

_____

_____

_____

What do I need to manage my emotions today?

_____

_____

_____

_____

_____

_____

EMOTIONS LIST

angry
annoyed
anxious
ashamed
awkward
brave
calm
cheerful
chill
confused
discouraged
disgusted
distracted
embarrassed
excited
friendly
guilty
happy
hopeful
jealous
lonely
loved
nervous
offended
scared
thoughtful
tired
uncomfortable
unsure
worried

Managing My Emotions

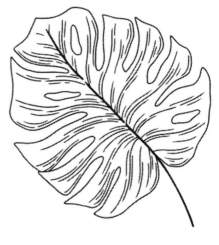

How did I react or respond today?

_____

_____

_____

_____

_____

What triggered my reaction or prompted my response?

_____

_____

_____

_____

_____

I am proud of myself because...

_____

_____

_____

_____

I am grateful for...

_____

_____

_____

_____

_____

Girl, I am in my feelings today!

MY DAILY EMOTIONS LOG

Choose two to three words from the list to describe how you feel today. Write them in the blank space below. Can't find your emotions there? Feel free to use other words.

Today's Date:

I think these feelings are:

○ both positive   ○ positive and negative
○ negative and positive   ○ both negative

I feel this way because _____

_____

_____

_____

_____

_____

_____

_____

What do I need to manage my emotions today?

_____

_____

_____

_____

_____

_____

EMOTIONS LIST
angry
annoyed
anxious
ashamed
awkward
brave
calm
cheerful
chill
confused
discouraged
disgusted
distracted
embarrassed
excited
friendly
guilty
happy
hopeful
jealous
lonely
loved
nervous
offended
scared
thoughtful
tired
uncomfortable
unsure
worried

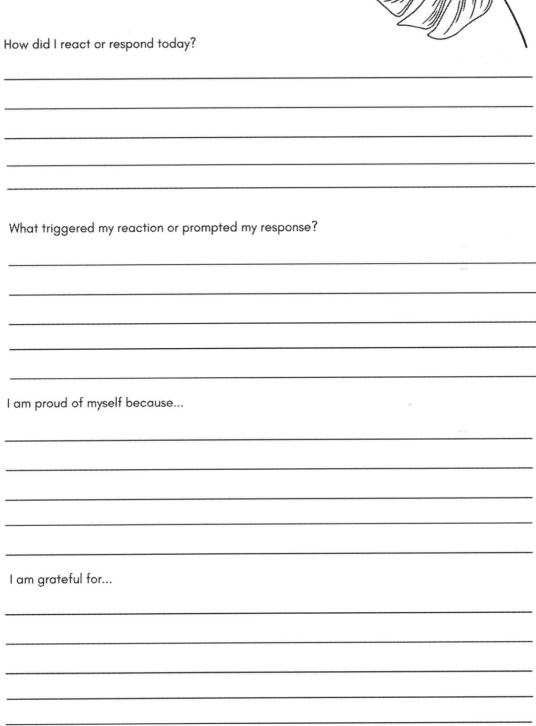

Managing My Emotions

How did I react or respond today?

_____
_____
_____
_____
_____

What triggered my reaction or prompted my response?

_____
_____
_____
_____
_____

I am proud of myself because...

_____
_____
_____
_____

I am grateful for...

_____
_____
_____
_____

Girl, I am in my feelings today!

MY DAILY EMOTIONS LOG

Choose two to three words from the list to describe how you feel today. Write them in the blank space below. Can't find your emotions there? Feel free to use other words.

Today's Date:

I think these feelings are:

○ both positive   ○ positive and negative

○ negative and positive ○ both negative

I feel this way because _____

_____

_____

_____

_____

_____

_____

_____

_____

What do I need to manage my emotions today?

_____

_____

_____

_____

_____

_____

_____

EMOTIONS LIST
angry
annoyed
anxious
ashamed
awkward
brave
calm
cheerful
chill
confused
discouraged
disgusted
distracted
embarrassed
excited
friendly
guilty
happy
hopeful
jealous
lonely
loved
nervous
offended
scared
thoughtful
tired
uncomfortable
unsure
worried

Managing My Emotions

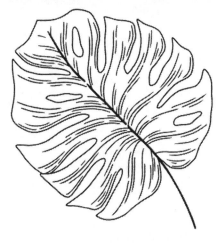

How did I react or respond today?

_____
_____
_____
_____
_____

What triggered my reaction or prompted my response?

_____
_____
_____
_____
_____

I am proud of myself because...

_____
_____
_____
_____
_____

I am grateful for...

_____
_____
_____
_____
_____

Girl, I am in my feelings today!

MY DAILY EMOTIONS LOG

Choose two to three words from the list to describe how you feel today. Write them in the blank space below. Can't find your emotions there? Feel free to use other words.

Today's Date:

I think these feelings are:

○ both positive

○ negative and positive

○ positive and negative

○ both negative

I feel this way because _____

_____

_____

_____

_____

_____

_____

_____

_____

What do I need to manage my emotions today?

_____

_____

_____

_____

_____

_____

_____

EMOTIONS LIST
angry
annoyed
anxious
ashamed
awkward
brave
calm
cheerful
chill
confused
discouraged
disgusted
distracted
embarrassed
excited
friendly
guilty
happy
hopeful
jealous
lonely
loved
nervous
offended
scared
thoughtful
tired
uncomfortable
unsure
worried

Managing My Emotions

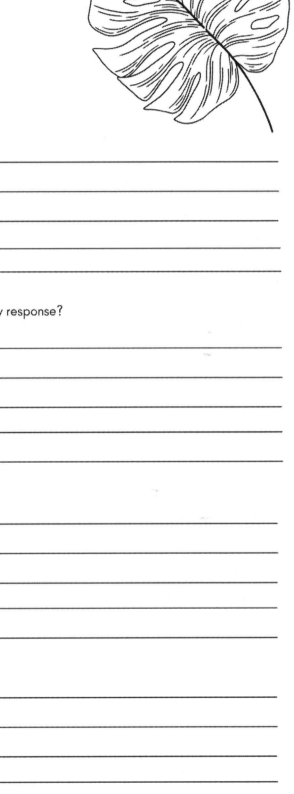

How did I react or respond today?

_____

_____

_____

_____

_____

What triggered my reaction or prompted my response?

_____

_____

_____

_____

_____

I am proud of myself because...

_____

_____

_____

_____

I am grateful for...

_____

_____

_____

_____

_____

GRATITUDE
&
Girlfriends
JOURNAL

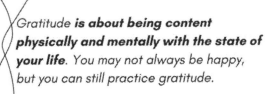

Gratitude **is about being content physically and mentally with the state of your life**. You may not always be happy, but you can still practice gratitude.

FINANCIAL Gratitude

"

ONLY BY *Giving* ARE YOU ABLE TO *Receive* MORE THAN YOU ALREADY HAVE.

— Jim Rohn

FINANCIAL *Gratitude*

From making six-figures to having a millionaire mindset, there seems to be an overwhelming amount of talk about money! Topics range from how much you have, how much do you want to make, to how much you need or don't have. Girlfriends, don't let nobody money shame you into thinking you don't have enough or you need to make more. Yes, we all could use a little more, well, a lot more money, however, financial gratitude is about being thankful for the financial resources we have and creating the atmosphere of expectation and responsibility for money to locate us! If you reflect on the life you have and what you've been given and earned, you will find yourself expressing financial gratitude. Sister girl, you are blessed even on your lowest bank account day so let's show some financial gratitude for your coins, cash, account balances, goals, ability, and seed!

Write out statements of gratitude regarding your financial well-being.

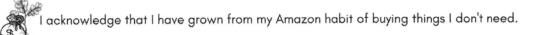 I am thankful that I have the skills to make money.

I am grateful to be responsible enough to pay my bills and/or invoices.

I acknowledge that I have grown from my Amazon habit of buying things I don't need.

Financial "GOAL"ITUDE

I WANT TO IMPROVE MY FINANCIAL WELL-BEING...

_____

_____

_____

_____

MY FINANCIAL GOALS

MY MOTIVATION

Financial "GOAL"ITUDE
ACTION PLAN

FINANCIAL GOAL	START DATE:	ACHIEVE BY:

GOAL PROGRESS: 0%   ☐☐☐☐☐☐☐☐☐☐   100%

ACTION STEPS

POSSIBLE OBSTACLES

HOW TO OVERCOME OBSTACLES

Financial "GOAL"ITUDE
ACTION PLAN

FINANCIAL GOAL	START DATE:	ACHIEVE BY:

GOAL PROGRESS: 0%   ☐☐☐☐☐☐☐☐☐☐   100%

ACTION STEPS

POSSIBLE OBSTACLES

HOW TO OVERCOME OBSTACLES

Financial "GOAL"ITUDE
ACTION PLAN

FINANCIAL GOAL	START DATE:	ACHIEVE BY:

GOAL PROGRESS: 0%   ☐☐☐☐☐☐☐☐☐☐   100%

ACTION STEPS	POSSIBLE OBSTACLES

HOW TO OVERCOME OBSTACLES

Financial "GOAL"ITUDE
ACTION PLAN

FINANCIAL GOAL	START DATE:	ACHIEVE BY:

GOAL PROGRESS: 0% □□□□□□□□□□□ 100%

ACTION STEPS

POSSIBLE OBSTACLES

HOW TO OVERCOME OBSTACLES

Financial "GOAL"ITUDE
ACTION PLAN

FINANCIAL GOAL	START DATE:	ACHIEVE BY:

GOAL PROGRESS: 0% ☐☐☐☐☐☐☐☐☐☐☐ 100%

ACTION STEPS	POSSIBLE OBSTACLES

HOW TO OVERCOME OBSTACLES

Financial "GOAL"ITUDE
ACTION PLAN

FINANCIAL GOAL	START DATE:	ACHIEVE BY:

GOAL PROGRESS: 0% [ ][ ][ ][ ][ ][ ][ ][ ][ ][ ] 100%

ACTION STEPS	POSSIBLE OBSTACLES

HOW TO OVERCOME OBSTACLES

Financial "GOAL"ITUDE
ACTION PLAN

FINANCIAL GOAL	START DATE:	ACHIEVE BY:

GOAL PROGRESS: 0% □□□□□□□□□□ 100%

ACTION STEPS	POSSIBLE OBSTACLES

HOW TO OVERCOME OBSTACLES

FINANCIAL *Gratitude*
MONEY MANTRA

Your financial gratitude comes with a plan and a purpose! Your attitude reflects your gratitude and the more you speak, believe, and put in the work everything you've written down will manifest. Before you know it, you'll be somebody's rich auntie (lol)! All jokes aside, read aloud and reflect on the money mantras below and use the blank bills to write your own financial affirmations.

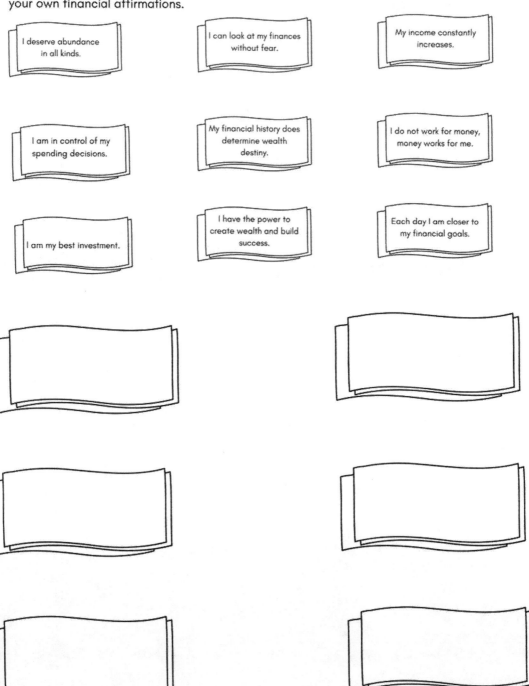

I deserve abundance in all kinds.

I can look at my finances without fear.

My income constantly increases.

I am in control of my spending decisions.

My financial history does determine wealth destiny.

I do not work for money, money works for me.

I am my best investment.

I have the power to create wealth and build success.

Each day I am closer to my financial goals.

This is the **gratitude effect**: a **ripple** of **acknowledgment** and **appreciation** that surges forward, **transforming** and inspiring us, and improving business outcomes. – Forbes

BUSINESS & CAREER *Gratitude*

LEARN TO BE *Thankful* FOR WHAT YOU ALREADY HAVE, WHILE YOU PURSUE ALL THAT YOU *Want.*

— Jim Rohn

Gratitude
BUSINESS & CAREER

Finding meaning in the work you've been created to do significantly increases your level of gratitude. Constantly reminding yourself of your why will bring you a greater sense of appreciation, value, and purpose in spite of the crazy co-worker, jealous manager, back-to-back meetings, or long hours. Although providing great customer service is a core value of most companies big or small, your gratitude should not limit itself to what service or products you provide. Your gratitude and appreciation for your business or career, possibly both, should extend to you! Understanding why you show up is just as important as how you show up and deserves to be acknowledged. Girlfriend, extend yourself gratitude and show yourself some kindness for sharing your gifts, skills, abilities, knowledge, and amazing power with the world.

Remind yourself how smart, wise, intelligent, talented, gifted, giving, credible, capable, and competent you are by writing your wins in the workplace and/or in your business in the spaces below.

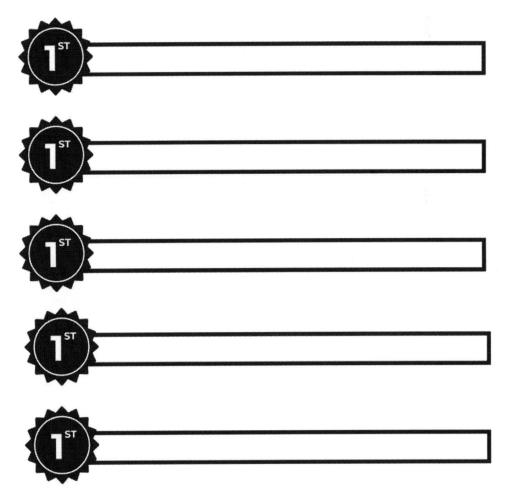

BUSINESS & CAREER

I am grateful to have a career/business that I...

_____

_____

_____

_____

_____

_____

_____

As it relates to my career/business, I find joy in...

_____

_____

_____

_____

_____

I am proud of myself because...

_____

_____

_____

_____

_____

My skills and helped me to...

_____

_____

_____

_____

_____

Gratitude
BUSINESS & CAREER

I do great work when it comes to...

_____
_____
_____
_____
_____
_____
_____
_____

You would be crazy not to hire me to...

_____
_____
_____
_____
_____

I am currently focused on...

_____
_____
_____
_____

I excited about my future because...

_____
_____
_____
_____
_____

GRATITUDE
&
Girlfriends
JOURNAL

GRATITUDE
&
Girlfriends
JOURNAL

*When we acknowledge the **small things** in **life**, we can **rewire our brain** to deal with the present with more awareness and broader perception.*

–Kristin Francis, MD

Gratitude

MENTAL HEALTH

"

MY DARK DAYS MADE

ME *strong* OR MAYBE I

ALREADY WAS *strong,*

AND THEY MADE ME

prove IT.

—Emery Lord

MENTAL HEALTH

Sis, your mental health encompasses your emotional, psychological, and social well-being, and influences your cognition, perception, and behavior (Wikipedia, Mental Health, 2022). Girlfriend, everything impacts your mental health and yet, you've survived 100 percent of your worst days! According Dr. Kristin Francis, studies have shown that expressing gratitude can positively change your brain.

Girl, what are you doing to protect your peace, your emotions, and your edges?

What comes to mind when you hear the words mental health?

What ways does your lifestyle ensure a healthy mental state?

What gets in the way of you making your mental health a priority?

What do you need to start or stop to make your mental health a priority?

What ways can you create a lifestyle to improve your mental health?

Gratitude
MENTAL HEALTH

Below are a few behaviors that can negatively impact your mental health.

CONSISTENTLY *pushing* YOURSELF BEYOND THE LIMIT

TRYING TO KEEP EVERYONE HAPPY

OVERTHINKING *everything*

STAYING IN THE PAST

SACRIFICING YOUR *health*

IGNORING *your* EMOTIONS

Below describe behaviors you demonstrate that negatively impact your mental health.

MENTAL HEALTH

What you think is ignited by what you believe. Your belief system is a culmination of your life journey. Where you grew up, your family, church, community, school, socio-economic status, and environment influences what you believe about yourself. Sister, you've done the work to change your narrative, but have you acknowledged and celebrated your growth with gratitude!

Celebrate below by sharing how you've rewired your belief system and improved your mental health!

LIMITING BELIEFS   ### UNLIMITING BELIEFS

CURRENT/PAST BELIEF   NEW BELIEF

CURRENT/PAST BELIEF   NEW BELIEF

CURRENT/PAST BELIEF   NEW BELIEF

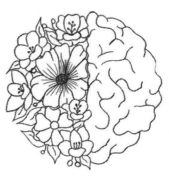

Gratitude
MENTAL HEALTH
I am Committed to Protecting Me!

Today, I am protecting my peace by...

_____
_____
_____
_____
_____
_____

I am grateful for healthy boundaries I set because they remind me...

_____
_____
_____
_____
_____

On my rest day(s) I plan to...

_____
_____
_____
_____
_____

I am taking better care of my mental health by...

_____
_____
_____
_____
_____

Affirmations of Gratitude for my MENTAL HEALTH

Read and speak the mental health affirmations aloud to show gratitude for your mental state. In the blanks, create your own mental health affirmations and recite them daily.

I don't have to believe
everything I think.

I have peace of mind
today.

I am not led by my
emotions.

_____

I am worth more than
someone's opionion.

I have clarity of mind.

_____

I make peace a priority.

I give myself permission rest.

_____

I am grateful to be able to
make decisions.

REST IS AN ACT OF Gratitude!

Sis, make time to rest. It's an act of gratitude to your body, mind, and soul!

What does rest mean to me?

_____

_____

_____

_____

_____

What does resting look like in my life?

_____

_____

_____

_____

_____

I find it difficult to rest because...

_____

_____

_____

_____

_____

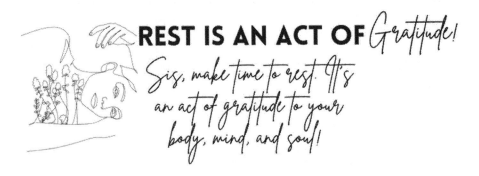

REST IS AN ACT OF *Gratitude!*

Sis, make time to rest. It's an act of gratitude to your body, mind, and soul!

Resting makes me feel...

_____
_____
_____
_____
_____

What does a healthy rest life balance look like for me?

_____
_____
_____
_____
_____

I will learn or have learned to rest because...

_____
_____
_____
_____
_____

THE GIFT OF *Gratitude*

Gratitude is an act of kindness or generosity that is demonstrated in our behavior or attitude. You must be intentional about showing yourself gratitude in every area and season of your life.

Girlfriend, set your intention to show gratitude to your future self by answering the following questions.

How will you demonstrate gratitude in your physical health?	
How will you continue to show gratitude for your spiritual well-being?	
How will you better manage your emotions?	
How will you show gratitude for your business and career?	
How do you plan to improve your financial portfolio?	
How will you improve your mental health?	
What do you want to be remembered for?	

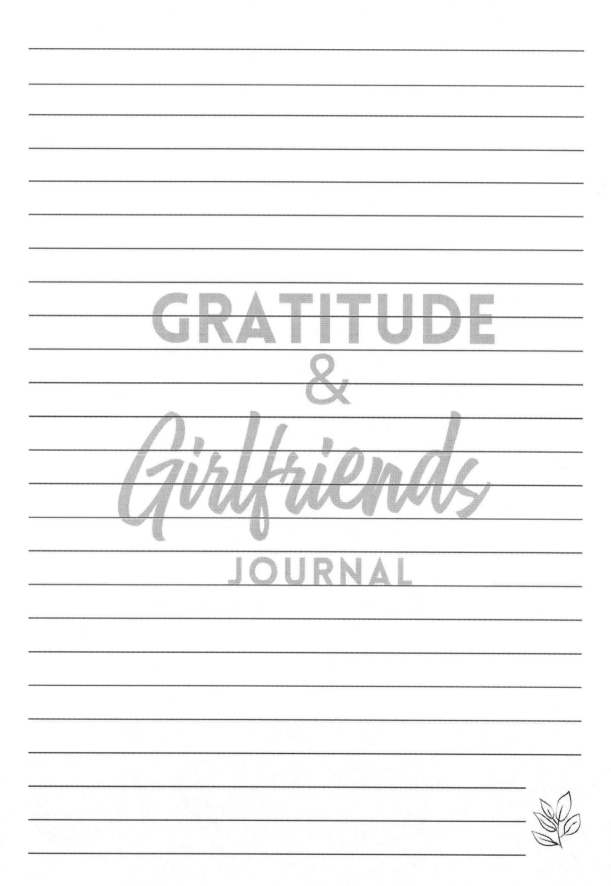

GRATITUDE
&
Girlfriends
JOURNAL

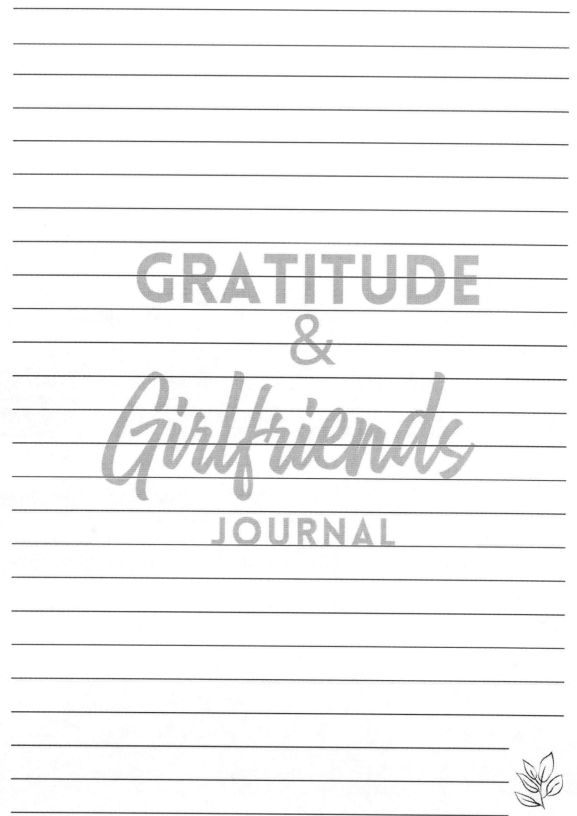

Girlfriends

A friend is one of the best things you can be and the
greatest things you can have.
- Unknown

GRATITUDE FOR THE *Girlfriends* WE DO LIFE WITH

TRACY GRIMES

Hey Girlfriend! We all need Girlfriends for various reasons throughout our lives. Some friends we admire for their perseverance through obstacles, call on them in times of need or just want to hang and chill or chit chat about what's happening in your life.

Some friendships have developed over time and some through fate because God knew you needed her for a specific season in your life. No matter the purpose or reason, here are some things we can do to show gratitude to the special girlfriends that we need or may need us as we navigate this whirlwind called "life". I hope the pages of this Girlfriends Section encourage you to celebrate your girlfriends, be a better friend and to step it up if you know you haven't been the friend you'd want to have.

Girlfriends

GO-TO GIRLFRIENDS

Let your intuition guide you in matters of the heart (love/friendships), though it's not your only tool for decision making, it's one of the most precise.

-Tracy Grimes

GO-TO GIRLFRIENDS

Checklist

Different seasons of life require different types of girlfriends and it's important that you know the season you're in and embrace the girlfriends assigned to walk through it with you. Take a look at the girlfriends go-to checklist to ensure you have your girls on deck!

- [ ] a girlfriend to talk to about your relationships
- [ ] a girlfriend to vent to and blowoff steam
- [ ] a girlfriend to talk to about wealth and finances
- [ ] a girlfriend who is wise and you can learn from
- [ ] a girlfriend to laugh with and just act up with
- [ ] a girlfriend to share your woes and worries with
- [ ] a girlfriend who is a prayer warrior
- [ ] a girlfriend that can talk you out of doing something crazy
- [ ] a girlfriend who is completely honest with you
- [ ] a girlfriend you can call in the middle of the night
- [ ] a girlfriend that motivates you and cheers you on
- [ ] a girlfriend you can brunch with
- [ ] a girlfriend who you can cry with
- [ ] a girlfriend who does not judge you and loves you for you
- [ ] a girlfriend who believes in you and won't let you fail

TELL YOUR *Girlfriends* TO PULL UP

Below make a list of your girlfriends and identify what season(s) she is assigned to in your life.

Girlfriend   **Season**

○ ....

○ ....

○ ....

○ ....

○ ....

Girlfriend   **Season**

○ ....

○ ....

○ ....

○ ....

○ ....

TELL YOUR *Girlfriends* TO PULL UP

Below make a list of your girlfriends and identify what season(s) she is assigned to in your life.

Girlfriend   **Season**

○ ....

○ ....

○ ....

○ ....

○ ....

Girlfriend   **Season**

○ ....

○ ....

○ ....

○ ....

○ ....

TELL YOUR *Girlfriends* TO PULL UP

Below make a list of your girlfriends and identify what season(s) she is assigned to in your life.

Girlfriend   **Season**

○ ....

○ ....

○ ....

○ ....

○ ....

Girlfriend   **Season**

○ ....

○ ....

○ ....

○ ....

○ ....

GRATITUDE
&
Girlfriends
JOURNAL

GRATITUDE
&
Girlfriends
JOURNAL

Girlfriends

GRATITUDE FOR MY GIRLS

True Girlfriends resists time, distance, and silence.
-Unknown

I AM GRATEFUL FOR MY GIRLFRIEND _____

I MET HER DURING A SEASON WHEN...

_____

_____

_____

_____

_____

_____

_____

_____

I AM GRATEFUL FOR HER ABILITY TO...

_____

_____

_____

_____

I CELEBRATE HER/I AM PROUD OF HER BECAUSE...

_____

_____

_____

_____

GRATITUDE & Girlfriends

I AM GRATEFUL FOR MY GIRLFRIEND _____

I MET HER DURING A SEASON WHEN...

_____

_____

_____

_____

_____

_____

_____

_____

I AM GRATEFUL FOR HER ABILITY TO...

_____

_____

_____

I CELEBRATE HER/I AM PROUD OF HER BECAUSE...

_____

_____

_____

_____

I AM GRATEFUL FOR MY GIRLFRIEND _____

I MET HER DURING A SEASON WHEN...

_____

_____

_____

_____

_____

_____

_____

I AM GRATEFUL FOR HER ABILITY TO...

_____

_____

_____

_____

I CELEBRATE HER/I AM PROUD OF HER BECAUSE...

_____

_____

_____

_____

GRATITUDE & *Girlfriends*

I AM GRATEFUL FOR MY GIRLFRIEND _____

I MET HER DURING A SEASON WHEN...

_____

_____

_____

_____

_____

_____

_____

_____

I AM GRATEFUL FOR HER ABILITY TO...

_____

_____

_____

_____

I CELEBRATE HER/I AM PROUD OF HER BECAUSE...

_____

_____

_____

_____

I AM GRATEFUL FOR MY GIRLFRIEND _____

I MET HER DURING A SEASON WHEN...

_____

_____

_____

_____

_____

_____

_____

_____

I AM GRATEFUL FOR HER ABILITY TO...

_____

_____

_____

_____

I CELEBRATE HER/I AM PROUD OF HER BECAUSE...

_____

_____

_____

_____

GRATITUDE & Girlfriends

I AM GRATEFUL FOR MY GIRLFRIEND _____

I MET HER DURING A SEASON WHEN...

_____

_____

_____

_____

_____

_____

_____

_____

I AM GRATEFUL FOR HER ABILITY TO...

_____

_____

_____

_____

I CELEBRATE HER/I AM PROUD OF HER BECAUSE...

_____

_____

_____

_____

I AM GRATEFUL FOR MY GIRLFRIEND _____

I MET HER DURING A SEASON WHEN...

_____

_____

_____

_____

_____

_____

_____

_____

I AM GRATEFUL FOR HER ABILITY TO...

_____

_____

_____

_____

I CELEBRATE HER/I AM PROUD OF HER BECAUSE...

_____

_____

_____

_____

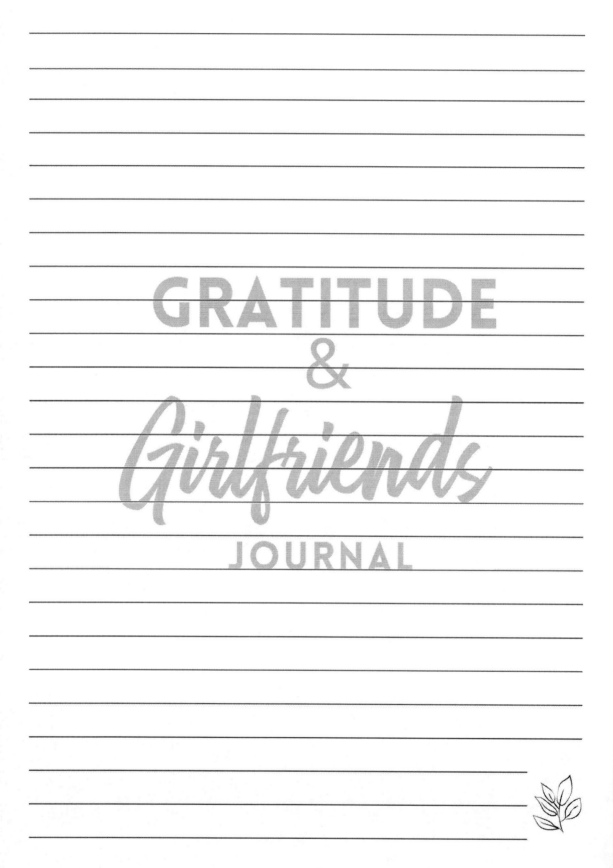

GRATITUDE
&
Girlfriends
JOURNAL

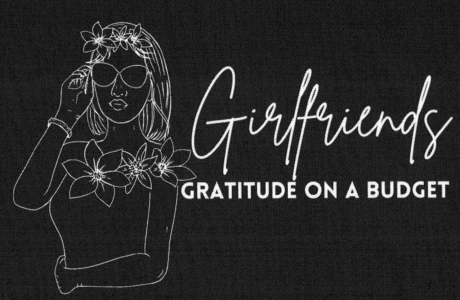

Girlfriends

GRATITUDE ON A BUDGET

*Sometimes friendship means to simply be there for your friend.
Not to give advice or try to fix anything. Just to be there and let
them know that they are cared for and supported.*
-A Good Unknown Girlfriend

WAYS TO SHOW GRATITUDE TO YOUR *Girlfriends!*

 Tell her what you think of her strengths.

 Offer to babysit.

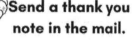 Send a thank you note in the mail.

 Send an affirmation text.

 Doordash her favorite meal.

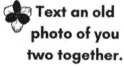 Text an old photo of you two together.

 Have coffee together or treat her to lunch.

 Send her flowers.

 Offer to cook dinner for her family one night of the week.

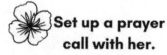 Set up a prayer call with her.

Girlfriends
BUDGET PLANNER

Showing gratitude cost you nothing, however, if you want to have a nice self-care experience, show your girlfriends some appreciation, or spend time with your girls, you will need to plan ahead. You can no longer allow your coins to keep you from living the life you want and deserve. We've provided this simple, but effective Girlfriend Budget Planner so you can enjoy yourself and your girlfriends.

Date :   Starting Balance :

List Item	Budget	Actual
Girls Night Out Dinner	$ 100.00	$50.00 *WE SPLIT THE BILL
Uber Eats Kimberly Starbucks	$ 20.00	$12.00
	$	
	$	
	$	
	$	
	$	
	$	
	$	
	$	

Total :

$Girlfriends
BUDGET PLANNER

Showing gratitude cost you nothing, however, if you want to have a nice self-care experience, show your girlfriends some appreciation, or spend time with your girls, you will need to plan ahead. You can no longer allow your coins to keep you from living the life you want and deserve. We've provided this simple, but effective Girlfriend Budget Planner so you can enjoy yourself and your girlfriends.

Date :   Starting Balance :

List Item	Budget	Actual
●	$	
●	$	
●	$	
●	$	
●	$	
●	$	
●	$	
●	$	
●	$	
●	$	

Total :

BUDGET PLANNER

Showing gratitude cost you nothing, however, if you want to have a nice self-care experience, show your girlfriends some appreciation, or spend time with your girls, you will need to plan ahead. You can no longer allow your coins to keep you from living the life you want and deserve. We've provided this simple, but effective Girlfriend Budget Planner so you can enjoy yourself and your girlfriends.

Date :   Starting Balance :

List Item	Budget	Actual
●	$	
●	$	
●	$	
●	$	
●	$	
●	$	
●	$	
●	$	
●	$	
●	$	

Total :

$Girlfriends
BUDGET PLANNER

Showing gratitude cost you nothing, however, if you want to have a nice self-care experience, show your girlfriends some appreciation, or spend time with your girls, you will need to plan ahead. You can no longer allow your coins to keep you from living the life you want and deserve. We've provided this simple, but effective Girlfriend Budget Planner so you can enjoy yourself and your girlfriends.

Date :   Starting Balance :

List Item	Budget	Actual
●	$	
●	$	
●	$	
●	$	
●	$	
●	$	
●	$	
●	$	
●	$	
●	$	

| Total : | | |

$ Girlfriends
BUDGET PLANNER

Showing gratitude cost you nothing, however, if you want to have a nice self-care experience, show your girlfriends some appreciation, or spend time with your girls, you will need to plan ahead. You can no longer allow your coins to keep you from living the life you want and deserve. We've provided this simple, but effective Girlfriend Budget Planner so you can enjoy yourself and your girlfriends.

Date :   Starting Balance :

List Item	Budget	Actual
●	$	
●	$	
●	$	
●	$	
●	$	
●	$	
●	$	
●	$	
●	$	
●	$	

Total :

$Girlfriends
BUDGET PLANNER

Showing gratitude cost you nothing, however, if you want to have a nice self-care experience, show your girlfriends some appreciation, or spend time with your girls, you will need to plan ahead. You can no longer allow your coins to keep you from living the life you want and deserve. We've provided this simple, but effective Girlfriend Budget Planner so you can enjoy yourself and your girlfriends.

Date :   Starting Balance :

List Item	Budget	Actual
●	$	
●	$	
●	$	
●	$	
●	$	
●	$	
●	$	
●	$	
●	$	
●	$	

Total :

BUDGET PLANNER

Showing gratitude cost you nothing, however, if you want to have a nice self-care experience, show your girlfriends some appreciation, or spend time with your girls, you will need to plan ahead. You can no longer allow your coins to keep you from living the life you want and deserve. We've provided this simple, but effective Girlfriend Budget Planner so you can enjoy yourself and your girlfriends.

Date :   Starting Balance :

List Item	Budget	Actual
•	$	
•	$	
•	$	
•	$	
•	$	
•	$	
•	$	
•	$	
•	$	
•	$	

Total :

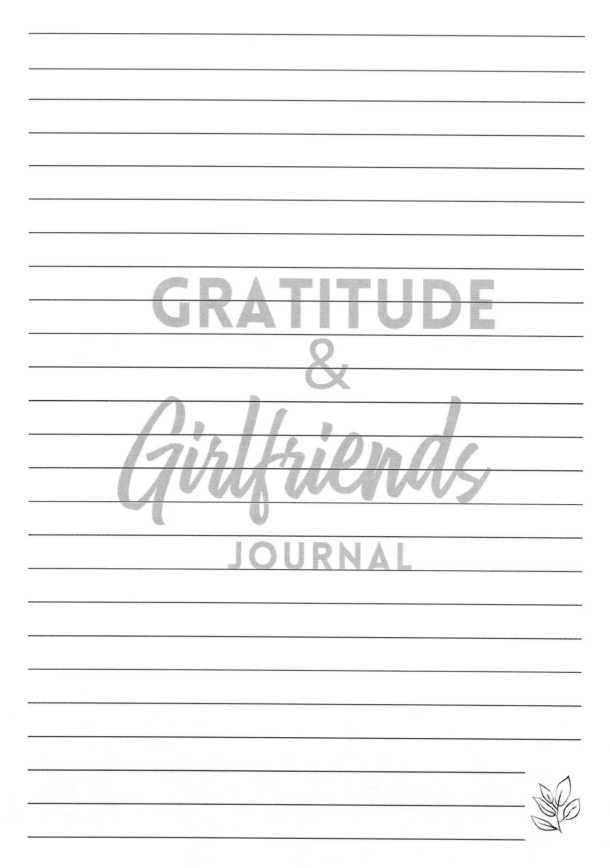

GRATITUDE
&
Girlfriends
JOURNAL

GRATITUDE
&
Girlfriends
JOURNAL

Girlfriends

THE DOS & DON'TS

A real girlfriend is one who walks in when the rest of the world walks out.
-An Unknown Girlfriend

Girlfriends DOS & DON'TS

Do

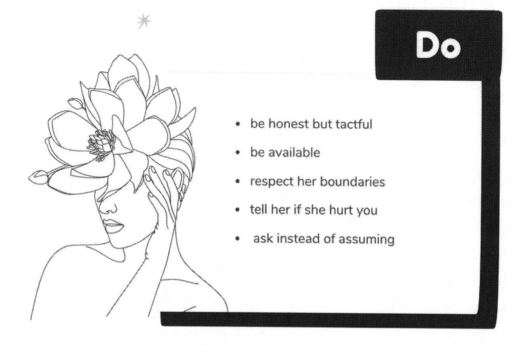

- be honest but tactful
- be available
- respect her boundaries
- tell her if she hurt you
- ask instead of assuming

Don't

- be judgmental
- assume you know her thoughts
- try to one-up her story with your story
- ghost her then show up and play the victim

Girlfriends DOS & DON'TS

Below write out your Girlfriend Dos and Don'ts.

Do

-
-
-
-
-

Don't

-
-
-
-
-

Tips to Grow Together as Girlfriends in Any Season!

It's ok not to be invited to every friend "outing"; it's not personal, it just may not be your season.

We all grow, accomplish, and succeed at different times in various areas of our lives and in our own time. Celebrate your girls in every season.

Remember, jealousy and gratitude cannot co-exist.

Be genuinely happy and excited for her wins while encouraging her during the losses.

Be reciprocal in the friendship; it should never be a one-sided relationship.

Never settle for a relationship where you have to be someone other than yourself.

with Love,
Tracy G.

GRATITUDE
&
Girlfriends
JOURNAL

Girlfriends
CHECK ON YOUR
STRONG FRIENDS

"This a wonderful day. I've never seen this one before."
Maya Angelou

GRATITUDE & *Girlfriends*

MENTAL HEALTH CHECK-IN

"Mental health...is not a destination, but a process. It's about how you drive, not where you're going."
— Noam Shpancer, PhD

Girlfriends, let's be honest. Sometimes we "ghost" our friends and cause harm to the relationship and most of the time neither person takes responsibility for the girlfriend "breakup." Yes, ghosting can destroy your relationship, however, before we give our sisters the gift of goodbye let's remember to do a mental health or wellness check-in because we never know what someone else is going through.

Below make a list of friends you need to reconnect with. Put them in the girlfriend categories below.

Strong Friends

_____

_____

Single Friends

_____

_____

Married Friends

_____

_____

Silent Friends

_____

_____

Grieving Friends

_____

_____

Girlfriend Check-up!

Using the list you created on the mental health check-in page begin your "Girlfriend Checkups."

DATE:

WHO DID I CHECK IN WITH TODAY?

THINGS I NEED TO FOLLOW-UP ON:

○ _____
○ _____
○ _____
○ _____

HOW DID I REACH OUT?

📞 PHONE CALL

💬 TEXT MESSAGE

✉ EMAIL

〰 VOICE TEXT

FACE TO FACE

WHAT IS THEIR CURRENT SEASON:

WHAT WE TALKED ABOUT:

WHAT TO PRAY FOR:

○ _____
○ _____
○ _____
○ _____
○ _____
○ _____

HOW WERE THEY FEELING TODAY?

😄 🙂 😐 🙁 ☹ 😫

Girlfriend Check-up!

Using the list you created on the mental health check-in page begin your "Girlfriend Checkups."

DATE:

WHO DID I CHECK IN WITH TODAY?

HOW DID I REACH OUT?

📞 PHONE CALL

💬 TEXT MESSAGE

✉️ EMAIL

🔊 VOICE TEXT

👥 FACE TO FACE

WHAT WE TALKED ABOUT:

HOW WERE THEY FEELING TODAY?

THINGS I NEED TO FOLLOW-UP ON:
○ _____
○ _____
○ _____
○ _____

WHAT IS THEIR CURRENT SEASON:

WHAT TO PRAY FOR:
○ _____
○ _____
○ _____
○ _____
○ _____
○ _____

Girlfriend Check-up!

Using the list you created on the mental health check-in page begin your "Girlfriend Checkups."

DATE:

WHO DID I CHECK IN WITH TODAY?

HOW DID I REACH OUT?

📞 PHONE CALL

💬 TEXT MESSAGE

📧 EMAIL

VOICE TEXT

🎭 FACE TO FACE

WHAT WE TALKED ABOUT:

HOW WERE THEY FEELING TODAY?

THINGS I NEED TO FOLLOW-UP ON:

○ _____

○ _____

○ _____

○ _____

WHAT IS THEIR CURRENT SEASON:

WHAT TO PRAY FOR:

○ _____

○ _____

○ _____

○ _____

○ _____

○ _____

Girlfriend Check-up!

Using the list you created on the mental health check-in page begin your "Girlfriend Checkups."

DATE:

WHO DID I CHECK IN WITH TODAY?

HOW DID I REACH OUT?

📞 PHONE CALL

💬 TEXT MESSAGE

✉ EMAIL

〰 VOICE TEXT

👥 FACE TO FACE

WHAT WE TALKED ABOUT:

HOW WERE THEY FEELING TODAY?

THINGS I NEED TO FOLLOW-UP ON:

○ _____
○ _____
○ _____
○ _____

WHAT IS THEIR CURRENT SEASON:

WHAT TO PRAY FOR:

○ _____
○ _____
○ _____
○ _____
○ _____
○ _____

Girlfriend Check-up!

Using the list you created on the mental health check-in page begin your "Girlfriend Checkups."

DATE:

WHO DID I CHECK IN WITH TODAY?

HOW DID I REACH OUT?

- PHONE CALL
- TEXT MESSAGE
- EMAIL
- VOICE TEXT
- FACE TO FACE

WHAT WE TALKED ABOUT:

HOW WERE THEY FEELING TODAY?

THINGS I NEED TO FOLLOW-UP ON:

- ○ _____
- ○ _____
- ○ _____
- ○ _____

WHAT IS THEIR CURRENT SEASON:

WHAT TO PRAY FOR:

- ○ _____
- ○ _____
- ○ _____
- ○ _____
- ○ _____
- ○ _____

Girlfriend Check-up!

Using the list you created on the mental health check-in page begin your "Girlfriend Checkups."

DATE:

WHO DID I CHECK IN WITH TODAY?

HOW DID I REACH OUT?

📞 PHONE CALL

💬 TEXT MESSAGE

✉️ EMAIL

🎙️ VOICE TEXT

🎭 FACE TO FACE

WHAT WE TALKED ABOUT:

HOW WERE THEY FEELING TODAY?

THINGS I NEED TO FOLLOW-UP ON:

○ _____
○ _____
○ _____
○ _____

WHAT IS THEIR CURRENT SEASON:

WHAT TO PRAY FOR:

○ _____
○ _____
○ _____
○ _____
○ _____
○ _____

Girlfriend Check-up!

Using the list you created on the mental health check-in page begin your "Girlfriend Checkups."

DATE:

WHO DID I CHECK IN WITH TODAY?

HOW DID I REACH OUT?

PHONE CALL

TEXT MESSAGE

EMAIL

VOICE TEXT

FACE TO FACE

WHAT WE TALKED ABOUT:

HOW WERE THEY FEELING TODAY?

THINGS I NEED TO FOLLOW-UP ON:

○ _____
○ _____
○ _____
○ _____

WHAT IS THEIR CURRENT SEASON:

WHAT TO PRAY FOR:

○ _____
○ _____
○ _____
○ _____
○ _____
○ _____

GRATITUDE
&
Girlfriends
JOURNAL

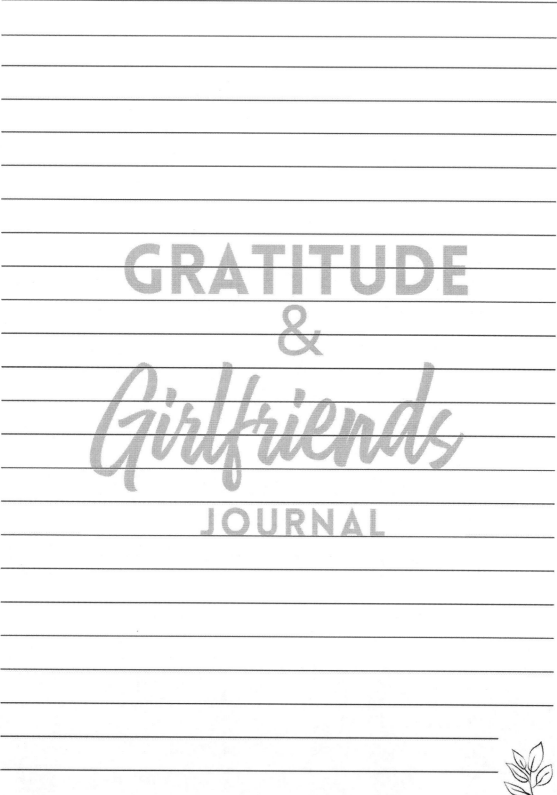

GRATITUDE
&
Girlfriends
JOURNAL